Contents

Answers to the questions are on the back of the Pull-out Poster in the centre of the book.

This book covers unit 5F from the year five scheme of work

Published by Coordination Group Publications Ltd.

Contributors:
Angela Billington
Chris Dennett
Lindsay Jordan
Tim Major
Katherine Stewart
Claire Thompson
Tim Wakeling
James Paul Wallis
Suzanne Worthington

ISBN 1-84146-278-0
Groovy website: www.cgpbooks.co.uk
Jolly bits of clipart from CorelDRAW
Printed by Elanders Hindson, Newcastle upon Tyne.

<u>*Sound*</u>

Sound can tell you <u>what</u> something is, and <u>where</u> it is.
That's how an owl can tell where a mouse is when it hears a squeak.

Q1 All these things make a sound. For each one, write the sound it makes in the bubble. Then write below it whether the sound is 'loud' or 'quiet'.

..tick tock..

.....quiet......

Q2 Moira, the police station cook, has been kidnapped and blindfolded by the fire brigade and stranded on a mountain. She can hear a police siren. The pictures show three places the car <u>could</u> be. For each picture, read what she's thinking about the noise then (circle) the right position of the car.

The siren is very quiet, but it's getting louder.

Now the siren is getting quieter.

Q3 Mr. Fisher's cat and dog are watching TV. When he opens the door and comes in, they point their ears towards the door. Why?

One Man And His Dog

I think we should all wear ear muffs.

Pardon?

Really loud noise can damage your hearing. That's why builders, racing drivers and airport ground crew wear ear protectors.

<u>*This page is OK — it's sound, man...*</u>

It's darn obvious that sound is ultra useful. Your ears can tell you <u>what</u> a sound is, and <u>where</u> it's coming from. It's handy for when you hear a <u>lion</u> roaring — you know where to <u>run away</u> from.

2

How to Make a Noise

All noise is made in the <u>same way</u> — by things <u>vibrating</u> (that means moving to and fro really quickly).

Q1 Put a ruler on the edge of a desk and hold it on the table with one hand. With the other hand, pull down the bit that's sticking over the edge and let go.

What do you see when you let go of the ruler?

What do you <u>hear</u> when you let go of it?

....

....

Q2 Stretch an elastic band with your hands. Get your friend to pluck it with a finger.

How does the elastic band move when your friend plucks it?

....

What do you hear?

....

Elizabeth liked playing with elastic bands.

mmm...
mmm...

Q3 Put your fingers on your throat (like in the picture). Then hum loudly.

What do you feel in your throat when you hum?

....

Q4 Fill in the gaps in this explanation of how sounds are made. Use some of the words below.

Loads of different things make sounds, but all for .... reason.

The .... is actually made by something ....

The vibration could be caused by .... something

or .... it.

TWANGING
HITTING
THE SAME
SOUND
CLARINET
VIBRATING
NO GOOD
A DIFFERENT

How to make a loud noise — step on your brother's toe...

Think of all the different things that make noises — <u>every</u> single noise you can think of is made by things moving and vibrating. Even when you whistle, the air is <u>vibrating</u> between your lips.

Sounds are Made When Things Vibrate

Anything that makes a noise does it by something <u>vibrating</u>.

Q1   Have a look at these pictures of a tuning fork being struck.

When you hit a tuning fork against a
solid object, it makes a ringing sound...

... and if you put it in water while it's still
ringing, the water sprays everywhere.

(Circle) the right words from the brackets to finish these sentences about what's happening.

When you hit a tuning fork against a table, it makes a (RINGING SOUND / WAILING NOISE).

That's because the prongs (VIBRATE / STAY STILL). You can tell that

(THE PRONGS ARE / YOUR HAND IS) vibrating because if you put the tuning fork into water

straight after hitting it, the water (SPRAYS EVERYWHERE / EVAPORATES).

Q2   Gertrude has just hit this cymbal. What is the
cymbal doing that causes it to make a noise?

Never touch glass with a
vibrating tuning fork. If you
did, it would shatter the glass.

....

What will she feel if she grabs
hold of the edge of the cymbal?

....

....

Q3   Helga has a drum with rice on it. When she
hits the drum, what'll happen to the rice?

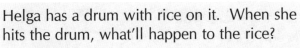

....

....

Q4   One last easy question. When something makes
a sound, what causes it? Circle the right answer.

Fred thought he had to
put <u>mice</u> on the drum...

IT'S SHOWING OFF   IT'S SHOUTING IN PAIN

SOMETHING'S VIBRATING   NOTHING

<u>Tuning fork? — No, I use a spoon for tuna...</u>

I hope you've got the message — <u>sound is caused by things vibrating</u>. If you've got that figured,
then you're doing fine. If not, then get it learnt. <u>Sound is caused by something vibrating</u>. Phew.

4

Sound Travels Through Things

Even though you can't <u>see</u> it, sound travels through <u>different things</u>.
It travels really easily through air, but it also travels through <u>other things</u>, like walls.

Q1   Write underneath each picture what the sound of the clock is travelling through to get to this man's ear.

....

....

Melted Chocolate

....

Hounds can't travel through walls.

tick tick

....

Q2   Look at this picture and work out what materials the sound from the noisy crow is travelling through to reach Mildred's ears.

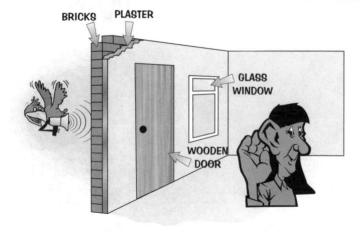

BRICKS   PLASTER

GLASS WINDOW

WOODEN DOOR

The sound is travelling through:

1)   *air* ....

2) ....

3) ....

4) ....

5) ....

An orchestra on tour — that's sound travelling...

Sound can travel through <u>almost anything</u>. Sometimes that's really handy, like if someone rings the doorbell when you're sat in a cupboard. Other times it's not so useful, like with noisy neighbours.

Sound Travels Through Things

Sounds can travel through loads of things — even water.

Q1 a) What 3 materials does the noise from Chris's stereo travel through before it gets to the dolphin?

....

....

....

b) What 4 materials does the noise from Chris's stereo travel through to get to the people in the submarine?

....

....

....

....

Q2 Anya and her monkeys are making a noise. There are two people and two fish who can hear it. Pick out the things from the list below that the noise has gone through to get to each one.

WATER   CLOTH   GLASS   AIR   METAL

WILMA THE FISH

1) ....

2) ....

3) ....

FATHER TOD, THE LORRY DRIVER

1) ....   2) ....   3) ....

DAVID THE SHEPHERD

1) ....

2) ....

Sound travels through water — good for Handel's water music...

Dolphins use sounds to find out where things are. They make <u>clicking noises</u> that travel through the sea, bounce off things and then come back to them. They can work out how far away something is, and which direction it's in. And they can use <u>whistling sounds</u> to 'talk' to other dolphins. Clever...

Sound Travelling

Sound travels much better through some materials than others. For example, you can speak to your brother if you stand on either side of a shut thin door, but you'd have to shout if you wanted him to hear you properly through the house <u>walls</u>.

Hannah and Colin are in different rooms. Both of the rooms have radiators in them, connected by water pipes. Hannah puts her ear to the radiator in her room, and Colin taps on the other radiator.

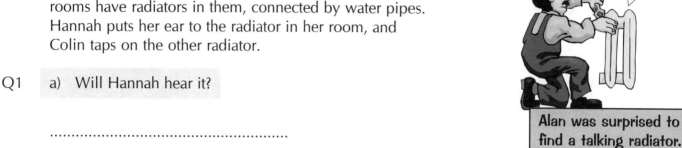

Can you hear me?

Alan was surprised to find a talking radiator.

Q1 a) Will Hannah hear it?

....

b) How does the sound travel from Colin's room to Hannah's room?

....

Josh and Aleesha have made a string telephone by poking a hole in the bottom of two yoghurt cartons and tying one end of a piece of string to one carton and one end to the other carton. Josh takes one end into another room (keeping the string tight) and talks into it. Aleesha can hear what Josh is saying.

Q2 Fill in the gaps in these sentences using some of the words in the carton (you don't need all of them).

worse

better   air

yoghurt

string

sound

carton

When Josh talks into the telephone, Aleesha can hear it

.... than when Josh talks without the

telephone. That's because the .... travels

through the ...., and it doesn't travel as

well through the ....

Q3 Whales can make sounds to communicate underwater. What does that tell you? Circle the right answer.

WATER MAKES
SOUNDS QUIETER.

WATER MAKES
WHALES CLEVER.

WATER MAKES
SOUNDS LOUDER.

SOUND CAN TRAVEL
THROUGH WATER.

Aleesha forgot to eat the yoghurt <u>before</u> making the phone.

Travelling sound — chatting in the car...

If you don't believe any of this, there's only one way to <u>check</u> — make a string telephone yourself. All you need is two yoghurt cartons and some string. Try the radiator test too.

Sound Travelling

When people say, 'Sound travels', they <u>don't</u> mean it catches the bus or train.
They mean it goes from one <u>place</u> to <u>another</u> — that's how you can hear it.

Q1 Sarah thinks sound travels just as well through any material. Her dog Kevin says that it travels better through some materials than others, because he can't hear things outside so well when the window's shut. Who is right?

....

Q2 a) I put a waterproof buzzer in different places to see if I'd still be able to hear it. Here's a table I started to fill in. Have a think about it and finish the table.

WHERE'S THE BUZZER?	In a closed wooden box	In an open wooden box	Buried under one metre of soil	In the bath (with water in)
CAN I HEAR THE BUZZER?	A bit			Fairly well

b) Fill in the gaps in these sentences, using the table to help.

Sound travels better through the box when it's .... than when it's

.... Sound travels a bit worse through .... than air.

It travels very badly through ....

Q3 I did the same test with my ticking clock — it's a bit quieter than the buzzer. Figure out what you think would happen this time and finish this table.

WHERE'S THE CLOCK?	On a table surrounded by air	Under a feather pillow	In a wooden cupboard	In a huge pile of sand
HOW WELL CAN I HEAR THE CLOCK?		Badly	A bit	

Q4 Sound travels better through some materials than others. Finish off these sentences using all the different materials from both tables — make sure you put them in the right place.

Sound travels really well through ....

Sound travels a bit through ....

Sound travels badly through ....

Sound materials — you can rely on them...

You can often hear stuff on the other side of a <u>wall</u> even though you can't see it. But the sound will always be <u>fainter</u> if it has to travel through stuff like walls or water — or even windows.

Stopping Sound from Travelling

Although you often want to hear sounds, sometimes you want to <u>stop</u> a sound completely.
I like to listen to music, but I have to <u>muffle</u> the sound of my yelling little brother.

Q1   Fill in the blanks in these sentences with words from the brackets.

Sometimes it's useful to stop sound travelling, because really ....

(quiet / loud) noises can .... (decorate / damage) your ears.

Fairly loud noises like footsteps in a school corridor can disturb people, so it's better if

the corridor makes the sound .... (more muffled / louder).

Q2   Match each reason for stopping sound travelling with a way
to stop it — join them up by drawing a line between them.

So you don't damage your ears.		Thick walls
So sound doesn't disturb neighbours.		Thick fluffy carpet
So footsteps don't disturb people.		Ear protectors

Q3   Hilda is hiking in her new steel boots. Put a tick next to
the places where her footsteps would sound very loud.

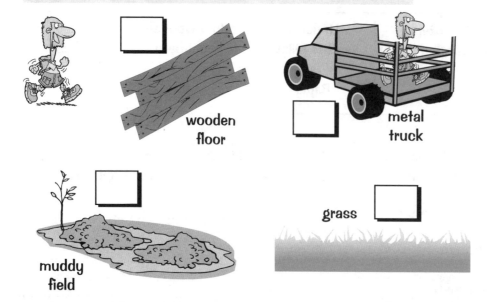

wooden floor

metal truck

muddy field

grass

Victor made sound travel by shouting and moving really fast.

Stop sound travelling — pinch its passport...

There are lots of ways to <u>muffle</u> sounds, like <u>padding</u> walls or floors. You can stop sounds getting
to your ears by wearing <u>ear protectors</u>. But you wouldn't hear people sneak up on you.

Materials for Muffling Sound

Professor Big-Hair and Professor Beehive have a problem.
They can't do any work, because their new teddy bear is
speaking to them, and they can't find the off switch.

Professor Big-Hair thinks if they <u>wrap</u> it in a sheet, they
can muffle the sound so they won't be able to hear it.

Professor Beehive thinks they should do an
experiment with <u>different materials</u>, to see
which one will muffle the sound <u>best</u>.

She says they should wrap the bear in each of the
materials, and see if they can <u>still hear</u> it speaking.

I HATE SMILING
I STINK
I EAT SPIDERS

ACE NASTY BEARS
GUARANTEED
TO BE 100% NASTY

Q1 Here are the materials the professors want to test. Put a tick ✔ next to each
material if you think it will be good at muffling the sound, and a cross ✘ if
you think it will be bad, then write <u>why</u> you think it will be good or bad.

	Newspaper	....
	Bubble wrap	....
	A winter coat	....
	A thick blanket	....
	A sheet	....
	A net	....

Materials To Test
1. Newspaper
2. Bubble Wrap
3. A Winter Coat
4. A Thick Blanket
5. A Sheet
6. A Net

Q2 Fill in the gaps in these sentences about the experiment.
Choose the right words from the boxes at the bottom.

OI!!

Bears don't like
you wrapping them
in blankets.

The professors should wrap the .... in each

.... they are testing. They should make sure they use

.... number of layers of each material, and that they

leave .... gaps when they wrap up the bear.

a tiny	bubble wrap	notebook	
some	no	a different	material
the same	bear	one or two	orang-utan

Talking teddies — I just can't bear them...

Sometimes it's <u>really useful</u> to be able to muffle sound — though if somebody is talking loudly
and you want to go to sleep, it might not be that easy to wrap them in a blanket. What a shame.

10

MINI-PROJECT

Materials for Muffling Sound

When you do an experiment, it's important to make sure that it's a <u>fair test</u>.

Q1 Choose words from the right to fill in the gaps in these sentences about <u>fair tests</u>.

Doing a 'fair test' means doing an experiment where you change only

.... To test which material muffles sound best, you must

only change the .... each time — you have to make sure that

you use the .... number of layers for each wrapping, that you've

used the same .... to muffle each time, and you measure how

.... it is in the same way each time. If you changed the

material and changed the number of layers as well, you ....

know if the result was because of the material or the number of layers.

always *same* *would* *weather* *sound* *two things* *material* *different* *loud* *your socks* *one thing* *warm* *wouldn't*

Q2 Look at these pictures of people trying to test which materials are good at muffling sound. Put a tick ✔ in the box if they are doing it properly (if it's a <u>fair test</u>). If it's not a fair test, put a cross ✘, and write what they're doing wrong on the dots.

I can't hear it in the sheet.

I can hear it in the blanket, so the sheet must be better at muffling the sound.

sheet   blanket

....
....
....
....

I can hear it in the sheet.

I can't hear it in the blanket, so the blanket must be better at muffling sound.

sheet   blanket

....
....
....
....

I can hear the bear in the blanket.

I can't hear the watch in the sheet, so the sheet must be better at muffling sound.

ticking watch

blanket   sheet

....
....
....

I can hear it in the sheet.

I can't hear it in the blanket, so the blanket must be better at muffling the sound.

sheet   blanket

....
....
....
....

Do a fair test — so no cheating...

You should be dead good at doing a fair test by now. It may seem as if I'm going on and on about it a lot, but if the test isn't <u>fair</u>, your results could be completely <u>wrong</u>. So it's really important.

Materials for Muffling Sound

Do the experiment from the last two pages. If you don't
have a nasty talking bear, then use something else that makes a sound.
Use a <u>ticking clock</u>, or something else that makes a noise that's
<u>not too loud</u> (if you use a huge foghorn, the materials might not be able to muffle the sound much).

Q1 Write down what you're going to use to make the noise (ticking clock or whatever).

....

Q2 Choose 4 materials to test (you could use some from Q1, page 9). Write them in the table.

Q3 Test a material by wrapping it round the ticking clock (or whatever you're using) and seeing how much you can still hear the noise. Write the result in the table, then test the next material.

(If you can't do the experiment, then use my Spare Results from the bottom of the page.)

MATERIAL	How Good It Was At Muffling Sound
....	
....	
....	
....	

Sam and Suze got carried away with the wrapping experiment...

Q4 Write the names of the materials, in order of how good they were at muffling the sound. (The quieter it made the sound, the better it was at muffling.)

Best: 2nd Best: 3rd Best: Worst:

....

Q5 If you tested any of the materials from Q1 on page 9, do your results match what you expected?

....

....

Spare Results: I tested a wind-up squeaky monkey toy. Winter Coat — couldn't hear it. Blanket — couldn't hear it. Bubble wrap — could hear it, but only quietly. Newspaper — could hear it the same as normal.

The sound of tea-cakes? — I said MUFFLE, not MUFFIN...

If you've used some of the materials from Q1 on p9 you can see if you were right back then when you tried to <u>guess</u> how good they'd be at muffling sound. That's a good way to do science — <u>guess</u> what'll happen, then come up with some <u>experiment</u> to <u>test</u> it and find out if you were <u>right</u>.

MINI-PROJECT

Materials for Muffling Sound

Dr. X and Dr. Z have done an experiment to test how good four different materials are at muffling the sound of a ticking clock.

They both did it by wrapping the clock in each of the materials, and seeing how many layers of it they needed before they couldn't hear the clock any more.

Here are their results:

Dr. X

Material	Layers Needed
Blanket	8
Cardboard	6
Duvet	4
Paper	10

Dr. Z

Material	Layers Needed
Blanket	8
Cardboard	7
Duvet	4
Paper	12

Q1   Did Dr. X and Dr. Z get the same results for all the materials?

YES ☐   NO ☐

Q2   Which materials did they get different results for? Write down those materials, and the results that Dr. X and Dr. Z got for them.

You might not need all the spaces, if they got the same results for some materials.

Material: ....

Dr. X's result: ....

Dr. Z's result: ....

Q3   When they got different results, was there a pattern? For example, was it always the same doctor who needed more layers than the other one? Explain what the pattern was, or write 'no' if there wasn't one.

....

....

Caroline used her mallet to make the clock stop ticking.

Q4   Can you think of any possible reasons why they got different results? If you said there was a pattern in Q3, think of reasons for that pattern.

....

....

And, to wrap this section up...

Two people doing an experiment won't always get <u>exactly</u> the same results. That isn't always a problem — unless one of them needs two layers of blanket and the other needs fifteen layers.

KS2 Science Answers — Changing Sounds

Page 14 The Pitch of a Drum

Q1: 3 — fairly high   1 — very low
    2 — fairly low   4 — very high

Q2: Highest: 4
                3
                2
                1
    Lowest: 5

Page 15 Pitch and Loudness

Q1: The "Hit it harder" box should be ticked.

Q2: The chick is making a **HIGH** sound. The sound is **QUIET**.
    Akiro's belly is making a **LOW** sound. The sound is **QUIET**.
    Maria is making a **HIGH** sound. The sound is **LOUD**.
    Wayne's truck is making a **LOW** sound. The sound is **LOUD**.

Q3: No, Aunt Ethel is wrong.

Q4: Pitch describes how **HIGH** or **LOW** a sound is. Both low and high sounds
    can be either **LOUD** or **QUIET**. Pitch has **NOTHING** to do with loudness.

Page 16 The Pitch of a Drum

Q1: The "get higher" box should be ticked.

Q2:

Page 17 The Pitch of Stringed Instruments

Q1: In order from highest pitch to lowest pitch:
    Violin, viola, cello, double bass.

Q2: In order from highest pitch to lowest pitch: C, A, B.

Page 18 The Pitch of Stringed Instruments

Q1:

Q2: To make the pitch of a drum higher, you could make the **SKIN** tighter. The
    pitch of a stringed instrument can be changed by using a different type of
    STRING. As well as making the string **SHORTER** or **THINNER**, you could
    make the pitch higher by **TIGHTENING** the string using the tuning pegs.

Page 19 The Loudness of Stringed Instruments

Q1: If you want to make a drum sound louder, you have to hit it **HARDER**. If
    you want to make a stringed instrument sound louder, you have to **PLUCK**
    the strings **HARDER**. Some string instruments are made by dragging a
    BOW across the strings to make them **VIBRATE**. To make a violin sound
    quieter you have to drag the bow **MORE SOFTLY** across the strings.

Q2: Quieter and higher: Pluck softer and tighten or shorten the string, press
    down on the string so a shorter length is vibrating, or use a thinner string.
    Louder and higher: Pluck harder and tighten or shorten the string, press
    down on the string so a shorter length is vibrating, or use a thinner string.
    Quieter and lower: Pluck softer and loosen or lengthen the string, press
    down on the string so a longer length is vibrating, or use a thicker string.

Page 20 Sound from Vibrating Air

Q1: Sound is caused by something **VIBRATING**. A guitar makes sound when
    the plucked **STRINGS** vibrate. When you beat a **DRUM** the skin vibrates to
    make the noise. In a wind instrument like a flute, it's the **AIR** inside that
    vibrates.

Q2: The "Blow harder" box should be ticked.

Q3: Sally is right.

Q4: **Either:** With string instruments the **LONGER** the string, the **LOWER** the pitch.
    Or: With string instruments the **SHORTER** the string, the **HIGHER** the pitch.
    And either: With wind instruments the **MORE** air there is to vibrate,
        the **LOWER** the pitch.
    Or: With wind instruments the **LESS** air there is to vibrate,
        the **HIGHER** the pitch.

Page 21 Sound from Vibrating Air

Q1:
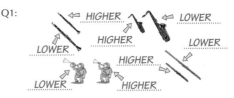

Q2 & Q3:

Page 22 Sound from Vibrating Air

Q1: You could change the amount of water in the bottle.

Q2:
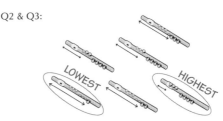

Page 23 Why Bells Ring

Q1: When you shake a bell, the **BALL** or **HAMMER** inside knocks against the
    outside. The noise is made by the **METAL** bit on the outside which
    VIBRATES when the hammer or ball hits it. The **HARDER** you shake the
    bell, the more it vibrates and the **LOUDER** it rings.

Q2: A small bell will make a **high** pitched sound. A large bell will make a **low**
    pitched sound. A medium sized bell will make a **medium** pitched sound.
    The **smaller** a bell is, the higher the pitch when you ring it.

Q3:

Page 24 Revision Questions

Q1: Ringing sound.

Q2: They vibrate.

Q3: It would shatter the glass.

Q4: Because the sound travels through the pipe better than through the air.

Q5: Ticks should be next to: Bubble wrap, A thick blanket, 4 thick sleeping bags

Q6: 4 thick sleeping bags

Q7: If you have two pieces of the same material the **THICKER** one will muffle
    sound better.

Q8: Doing a 'fair test' means doing an experiment where you change only
    ONE THING. To test which material muffles sound best, you must only
    change the **MATERIAL**.

Page 25 Revision Questions

Q9: Big Drum: **low pitch**, Very Small Drum: **high pitch**, Tin Whistle: **high
    pitch**, Violin: **high pitch**, Tuba: **low pitch**.

Q10: Pitch describes how **HIGH** or **LOW** a sound is. Both low and high sounds
     can be either **QUIET** or **LOUD**. The pitch of a sounds tells you
     NOTHING about its loudness.

Q11: a) A   b) C   c) By plucking the string harder. d) HIGHER

Q12: Sound is caused by something **VIBRATING**. A guitar makes sound when
     the plucked **STRINGS** vibrate. When you beat a drum the **SKIN** vibrates
     to make the noise. In a wind instrument, it's the **AIR INSIDE** that vibrates.

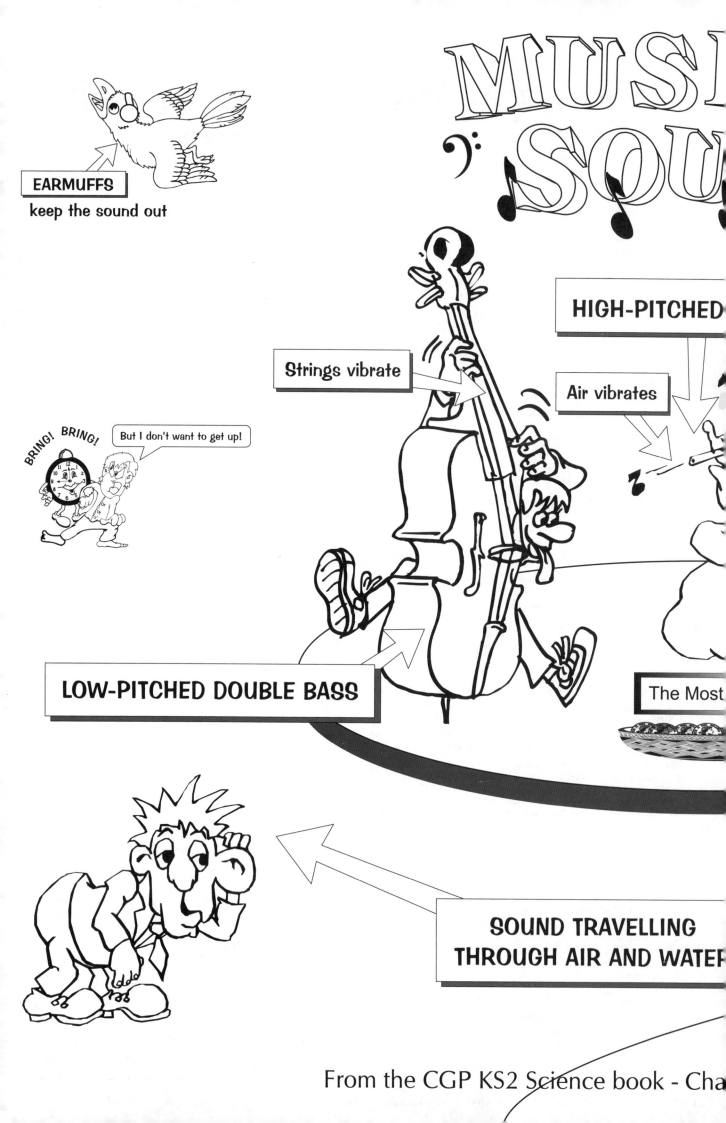

EARMUFFS
keep the sound out

MUSI...
SOU...

HIGH-PITCHED

Strings vibrate

Air vibrates

BRING! BRING!
But I don't want to get up!

LOW-PITCHED DOUBLE BASS

The Most

SOUND TRAVELLING
THROUGH AIR AND WATER

From the CGP KS2 Science book - Cha...

KS2 Science Answers — Changing Sounds

Page 1 Sound

Q1:
quiet   loud   quiet   loud

Q2:

Q3: Because they hear a sound and point their ears to the door to hear better.

Page 2 How to Make a Noise

Q1: The ruler moves up and down until it slows down and stops.
You can hear a twanging noise.

Q2: The elastic band wobbles back and forth until it slows down and stops.
You can hear a twanging noise again.

Q3: You can feel a vibration or slight tickly feeling.

Q4: Loads of different things make sounds, but all for **THE SAME** reason. The **SOUND** is actually made by something **VIBRATING**. The vibration could be caused by **HITTING** something or **TWANGING** it.

Page 3 Sounds are Made When Things Vibrate

Q1: When you hit a tuning fork against a table, it makes a **RINGING SOUND**. That's because the prongs **VIBRATE**. You can tell that **THE PRONGS ARE** vibrating because if you put the tuning fork into water straight after hitting it, the water **SPRAYS EVERYWHERE**.

Q2: The cymbal vibrates to make a noise.   She will feel the cymbal vibrating.

Q3: The rice will fly up in the air.

Q4: 'SOMETHING'S VIBRATING' should be circled.

Page 4 Sounds Travels Through Things

Q1: air   water
melted chocolate
pillow (feathers)

Q2: air, glass, wood, bricks, plaster

Page 5 Sounds Travels Through Things

Q1: a) rubber, air, water   b) rubber, air, water, metal

Q2: Wilma the Fish: air, glass, water
Father Tod, the Lorry Driver: air, glass, metal
David the Shepherd: air, cloth

Page 6 Sound Travelling

Q1: a) Yes.   b) The vibration travels along the water pipe (through the water and metal).

Q2: When Josh talks into the telephone, Aleesha can hear it **BETTER** than when Josh talks without the telephone. That's because the **SOUND** travels through the **STRING**, and it doesn't travel as well through the **AIR**.

Q3: Sound can travel through water.

Page 7 Sound Travelling

Q1: Kevin the dog is right.

Q2: a)

WHERE'S THE BUZZER?	In a closed wooden box	In an open wooden box	Buried under one metre of soil	In the bath (with water in)
CAN I HEAR THE BUZZER?	Just about	Yes	No	Fairly well

b) Sound travels better through the box when it's **OPEN** than when it's **CLOSED**. Sound travels a bit worse through **WOOD** than air. It travels very badly through **SOIL**.

Q3:

WHERE'S THE CLOCK?	On a table	Under a pillow	In a cupboard	In a huge pile of sand
HOW WELL CAN I HEAR THE CLOCK?	Very well	Badly	A bit	Not at all

Q4: Sound travels really well through **AIR**.
Sound travels a bit through **WOOD** and **WATER**.
Sound travels badly through **SOIL**, **FEATHERS** and **SAND**.

Page 8 Stopping Sound from Travelling

Q1: Sometimes it's useful to stop sound travelling, because really **LOUD** noises can **DAMAGE** your ears. Fairly loud noises like footsteps in a school corridor can disturb people, so it's better if the corridor makes the sound **MORE MUFFLED**.

Q2:

Q3: 'Wooden floor' and 'metal truck' should be ticked.

Page 9 Materials for Muffling Sound

Q1: ✘ Newspaper — because it is very thin.
✔ Bubble wrap — because it has loads of layers of plastic.
✔ A Winter coat — because it is thick and padded.
✔ A thick blanket — because it is padded.
✘ A sheet — because it is very thin.
✘ A net — because it has lots of holes in it.

Q2: The professors should wrap the **BEAR** in each **MATERIAL** they are testing. They should make sure they use **THE SAME** number of layers of each material, and that they leave **NO** gaps when they wrap up the bear.

Page 10 Materials for Muffling Sound

Q1: Doing a fair test means doing an experiment where you change only **ONE THING**. To test which material muffles sound best, you must only change the **MATERIAL** each time — you have to make sure that you use the **SAME** number of layers for each wrapping, that you've used the same **SOUND** to muffle each time, and you measure how **LOUD** it is in the same way each time. If you changed the material and changed the number of layers as well, you **WOULDN'T** know if the result was because of the material or the number of layers.

Q2: Top left: ✘ One of the scientists is standing further away than the other one.
Top right: ✔ This is a fair test.
Bottom left: ✘ The scientists are using two different sounds.
Bottom right: ✘ The bear is wrapped in more layers of blanket than of sheet

Page 11 Materials for Muffling Sound

Q1: The gap should be filled in with the choice of sound.

Q2: The table should be filled in with the names of the four materials to be tested

Q3: The table should be filled in with their results. I've put my spare results in to give you an idea of what they should look like.

MATERIAL	How Good It Was At Muffling Sound
Winter Coat	Couldn't hear it.
Blanket	Couldn't hear it.
Bubble Wrap	Could hear it, but only quietly.
News-paper	Could hear it the same as normal.

Q4: The gaps should be filled in with the materials in order of their ability to muffle. Here's my spare results again:
Best — winter coat & blanket (joint best)
3rd Best — bubble wrap
Worst — newspaper

Q5: The gap should be filled in, or not, depending on their answers on page 9.

Page 12 Materials for Muffling Sound

Q1: No.

Q2: Material: Cardboard   Paper
Dr. X's result: 6   10
Dr. Z's result: 7   12

Q3: Pattern — Dr. Z needed more layers when there were different results.

Q4: Dr. Z may be a little hard of hearing, she may be standing further away from the clock than Dr. X is, or Dr. X might have left gaps in the wrapping. There could be other reasons — accept any reasonable answers.

Page 13 Pitch Means How High

Q1: The pitch of a note is how high or how **LOW** it is. A whistle makes a **HIGH**-pitched sound. A bass-drum makes a **LOW**-pitched sound. A good example of a high-pitched sound is a **MOUSE SQUEAKING**.

Q2:

Bass Saxophone
Low Pitch

Piccolo
High Pitch

Tuba
Low Pitch

Drum
Low Pitch

Violin
High Pitch

Pitch Means How High

A sound can be <u>high pitched</u> or <u>low pitched</u>. A bird cheeping is
high pitched and my stomach rumbling is low pitched.

Q1   Use some of the words in the oval to fill in the gaps.

The pitch of a note is how high or how .... it is.

A whistle makes a .... pitched sound.

A bass-drum makes a .... pitched sound.

A good example of a high pitched sound is a

....

low   mouse squeaking   hard   low
   high   loud   cow mooing

Squeak!

Rumble!

Roger the Mouse
wondered if he could
hear thunder...

Q2   For each of these instruments, write 'high pitch' or 'low pitch' underneath its name.

Tuba

....

Piccolo

....

Bass Saxophone

....

Violin

....

Drum

....

Did You
Know?

Human ears can only hear sounds up to a
certain pitch. Dog trainers use special whistles
that are so high people can't hear them.

Limbo dancing music — hits really low notes...

It's got nothing to do with cricket. A <u>high pitched note</u> is a <u>high note</u> and a <u>low pitched note</u> is
a <u>low note</u>. Nothing harder than that. People add 'pitch' on to make it sound more <u>impressive</u>.

The Pitch of a Drum

Drums are great for making loads of noise. They come in all different shapes and sizes and each of them has its own sound. A drum's pitch depends on its <u>size</u>.

Q1 Douglas tried playing several drums. Some of them made high sounds and some made low sounds. Number all the drums in order of how low or high their pitch is. Start with '1' in the box next to the drum with the lowest pitch and go up to '4' next to the highest pitched drum.

fairly high

very low

Hank's gran had got it wrong again.

DRUMSTICKS

fairly low

very high

Q2 Here are some more drums. Which one will be the highest? Which one will be the lowest? Write down the numbers of the drums, putting them in order of how high pitched they are.

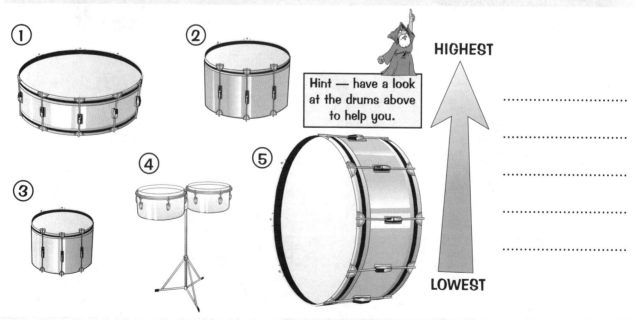

Hint — have a look at the drums above to help you.

HIGHEST

....

....

....

....

....

LOWEST

What's a hunter's favourite drum? — a snare drum...

As far as drums go, bigger means lower — the <u>bigger</u> the drum the <u>lower</u> the pitch. And the same the other way round — <u>smaller</u> means <u>higher</u>. That's why drum kits have different sized drums.

Pitch and Loudness

So now you know a fair bit about how the size of a drum affects its pitch.
The other thing that is different on different instruments is how <u>loud</u> they are.

Q1 Bertie is hitting a drum, but wants to make it sound louder. Choose the
best way for him to do this from the phrases below and tick the box.

Paint the drum a different colour [ ]

Use a softer stick [ ]

Hit it harder [ ]

Shout at the drum [ ]

Hit it more often [ ]

Q2 Look at the pictures below and decide whether the sounds being made are
loud or quiet, high or low. Circle the right words to finish the sentences.

The chick is making a high / low sound.
The sound is loud / quiet.

Akiro's belly is making
a high / low sound.
The sound is loud / quiet.

MINI RUMBLE

Maria is making
a high / low sound.
The sound is loud / quiet.

Wayne's truck is making
a high / low sound.
The sound is loud / quiet.

Q3 My Aunt Ethel reckons all high sounds
are quiet and all low sounds are loud.
Is she right? ....

Q4 Using the words in the boxes, fill in the blanks to
complete this paragraph about <u>pitch</u> and <u>loudness</u>.

HIGH

Pitch describes how .... or

NOTHING

.... a sound is. Both low and high sounds can

LOUD

be either .... or ....

LOW

Pitch has .... to do with loudness.

QUIET

<u>You'll have to speak up — I can't hear you...</u>

Yeah, I know it can get a bit confusing. It seems to make sense that a high-pitched sound would be
quiet and a low-pitched sound would be loud — but that's <u>not true</u>. <u>Any</u> pitch can be loud or quiet.

The Pitch of a Drum

Yet more about drums on this page — this time it's about the <u>tightness</u> of the <u>skin</u>.
Drums sound <u>higher</u> if their skin is pulled <u>tighter</u>, and they sound lower if their skin is slacker.

Q1 If I turn the screws on this drum so that the skin is pulled downwards at the edges, what will happen to the sound? Tick ✔ the box next to the right answer.

It'll get louder ☐

It'll get lower ☐

It'll get higher ☐

It'll get darker ☐

It'll go green ☐

It'll get quieter ☐

Q2 On this beautiful shiny drum kit, label which drums will have a high pitch, which will be medium and which will have a low pitch.

Watch out — they're different sizes as well as tight or slack

Write HIGH, MEDIUM or LOW in the boxes to label each drum.

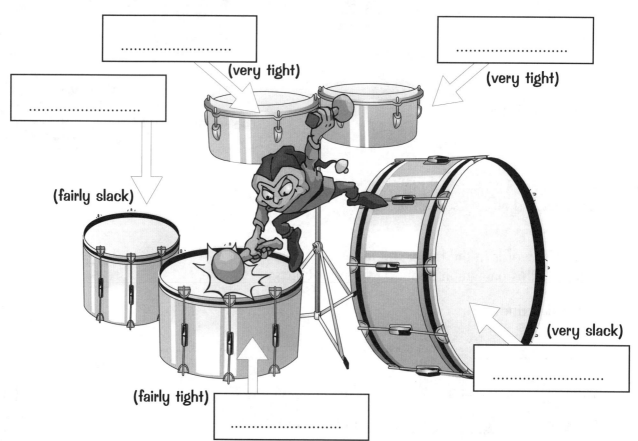

.... (very tight)

.... (very tight)

....

(fairly slack)

(very slack)

....

(fairly tight)

....

Aim high — don't be a slacker...

More things about sound that go in pairs. This time, the <u>tighter</u> the <u>higher</u>, and the <u>slacker</u> the <u>lower</u>.
So a big drum with a slack skin would make a <u>really</u> low-pitched noise if you hit it. Phew...

The Pitch of Stringed Instruments

You know that a drum sounds <u>higher</u> if the skin is <u>smaller</u>. The same sort of thing happens with <u>stringed instruments</u> — the sound is <u>higher</u> if the string is <u>shorter</u>.

Q1 Take a look at these different stringed instruments, and write them in order of pitch, with the highest pitch first.

Thinking about the size of each instrument should help.

 cello

 viola

 violin

 violin / double bass

....

Highest Pitch   Lowest Pitch

It would be pretty tricky playing an instrument if you had to change the strings when you wanted to play different pitches. You can change the pitch of a note on an instrument like a guitar by pressing down on the string at different places. For example, pressing higher up on a guitar shortens the bit of string that's vibrating — so it's like having a shorter string.

Q2 Jimbo is playing some heavy metal on his new guitar. Write the letters from each picture in order of pitch — with the highest pitch first.

Highest Pitch ....

....

Lowest Pitch ....

Remember: He doesn't play this bit

He plays this bit.

Jimbo couldn't get any pitch at all out of his old guitar.

Guitars playing football — on a musical pitch...

Okay, there are a few things to remember. You can change the pitch of a stringed instrument — <u>shorter strings</u> give <u>higher</u> pitches, and you can change the <u>length</u> by pressing the string down.

The Pitch of Stringed Instruments

The pitch of a stringed instrument <u>doesn't</u> just depend on <u>length</u> — it also depends on the <u>thickness</u> of the string. The <u>thicker</u> the string is, the <u>lower</u> the pitch will be.

Q1   For each pair of strings, put a tick next to the one that would have the highest pitch.

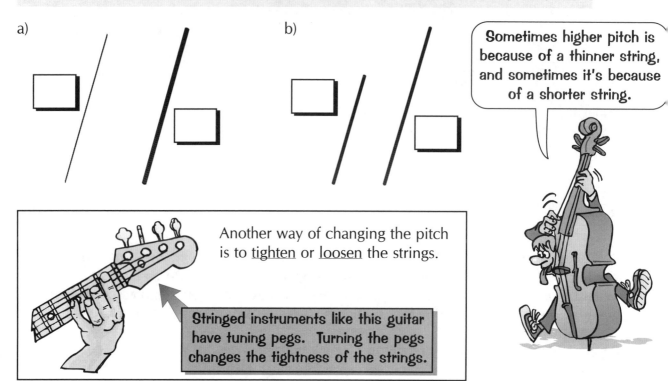

a)

b)

Sometimes higher pitch is because of a thinner string, and sometimes it's because of a shorter string.

Another way of changing the pitch is to <u>tighten</u> or <u>loosen</u> the strings.

Stringed instruments like this guitar have tuning pegs. Turning the pegs changes the tightness of the strings.

Q2   Fill in the gaps using the words on the cello.

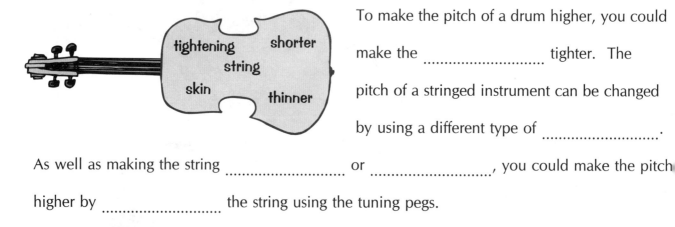

tightening   shorter   string   skin   thinner

To make the pitch of a drum higher, you could make the .... tighter. The pitch of a stringed instrument can be changed by using a different type of ....

As well as making the string .... or ...., you could make the pitch higher by .... the string using the tuning pegs.

Nikki found a different way to tighten her guitar strings.

STRETCH

Tuning competition — Clash of the Tightens...

There's quite a lot here you really ought to know. You need to know the three things you can do to a string to change the pitch — change the <u>length</u>, change the <u>thickness</u> or <u>tighten</u> the string.

The Loudness of Stringed Instruments

Music would be dead boring if it didn't have <u>loud</u> bits and <u>quiet</u> bits.
Violin players have to know how to make their instruments sound <u>louder</u> or <u>quieter</u>.

Q1 (Circle) the right words to finish off this paragraph about <u>loudness</u>.

If you want to make a drum sound louder, you have to hit it HARDER / SOFTER . If you want

to make a stringed instrument sound louder, you have to HIT / PLUCK the strings

HARDER / MORE SOFTLY . Some string instruments are played by dragging a CAT / BOW

across the strings to make them VIBRATE / SHORTER . To make a violin sound quieter you

have to drag the bow HARDER / MORE SOFTLY across the strings.

Q2 Write how you would change the sound of a guitar string in
the four ways listed below. I've done one to start you off.

Remember that there are <u>three</u> ways to
change the pitch. Don't be boring. Try
to use all of them in your answers.

Louder and lower: ....*Pluck harder and loosen the string.*.........

Quieter and higher: ....

Louder and higher: ....

Quieter and lower: ....

The Twangers never worried much
about playing their guitars quieter.

I can't turn up the volume — I'm not a-loud...

As well as being able to change the <u>pitch</u> of a sound from a stringed instrument, you should
know how to change the <u>loudness</u>. Now all you need to do is learn to play something.

Sound from Vibrating Air

If you've done the last few pages, you know about pitch in <u>stringed instruments</u>.
This page is about pitch in <u>wind instruments</u>.

Q1 Use the words in the snake charmer's box underneath to fill in the gaps
in these sentences. Be careful though, you don't need all of them.

Sound is caused by something .... A guitar makes sound when the plucked

.... vibrate. When you beat a .... the skin vibrates to make the

noise. In a wind instrument like a flute, it's the .... inside that vibrates.

WATER   DRUM

CHICKEN DRUMSTICK

CHICKENS   AIR

VIBRATING

STRINGS

DANCING

Q2 Ben is playing a mouth organ. He wants to make it
louder, what should he do? Tick ✔ the right answer.

> Ben was also very
> good at playing the
> *mouse* organ.

Blow softer. ☐   Blow harder. ☐

Squeeze the mouth organ tightly. ☐

Use his nose instead of his mouth. ☐

Q3 Raj thinks that how high a wind instrument sounds depends on how much air
you can hold in your lungs. Sally thinks it's to do with how much air is vibrating.

Which of them is right? ....

Q4 Fill in the gaps using one of the words from the brackets.

With string instruments the .... (LONGER / SHORTER) the

string, the .... (HIGHER / LOWER) the pitch.

With wind instruments the .... (MORE / LESS) air

there is to vibrate, the .... (HIGHER / LOWER) the pitch.

A blow by blow account of wind instruments...

The main thing to get to grips with on this page is that the <u>pitch</u> of a wind instrument depends
on the <u>amount of air</u> inside it — that's why a trombone makes a lower sound than a recorder.

Sound from Vibrating Air

OK, this is how it works — the <u>more</u> air that is vibrating, the <u>lower</u> the pitch.
So, the <u>longer</u> the pipe of a wind instrument is, the <u>lower</u> it will sound.

Q1 Each of these pictures shows different sizes of the same kind of instrument — for each pair write 'HIGHER' or 'LOWER' next to the right instrument to describe their pitch.

Q2 Here are some pictures of flutes with open and closed keys. Draw a line next to each flute to show how long the air column would be. I've done one to show you what I mean.

Remember — the longer the air column, the lower the pitch. You can tell how much air is making the sound — it starts at the mouthpiece and stops at the first open key

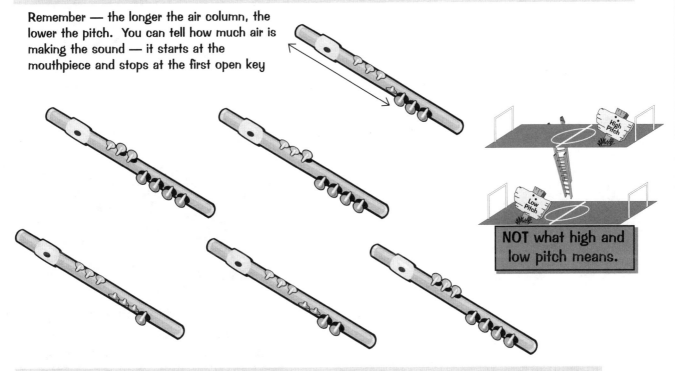

NOT what high and low pitch means.

Q3 Have another look at the pictures above and circle the flute with the lowest pitch and the one with the highest pitch and write 'HIGHEST' and 'LOWEST' next to them.

High pitched — football on the aeroplane...

Even if you can't play one, you ought to know how different pitches are made with an instrument like a flute. It's not complicated — the <u>more</u> air vibrating, the <u>lower</u> the sound. It's that simple.

Sound from Vibrating Air

You may well know that you can make a musical instrument just by <u>blowing</u> across the top of a bottle with a bit of <u>water</u> in it — and if you didn't, I'm telling you now.

Q1 The pitch of the sound you get when you blow over the bottle depends on how much air is vibrating — just like any other musical instrument. Shade in red the air that would be vibrating in this picture.

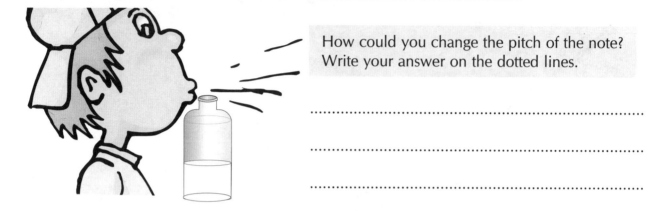

How could you change the pitch of the note? Write your answer on the dotted lines.

....

....

....

Q2 Here are some more pictures of bottles which could be played by blowing over them. Number them in order of pitch staring with 1 as the lowest and with 7 as the highest.

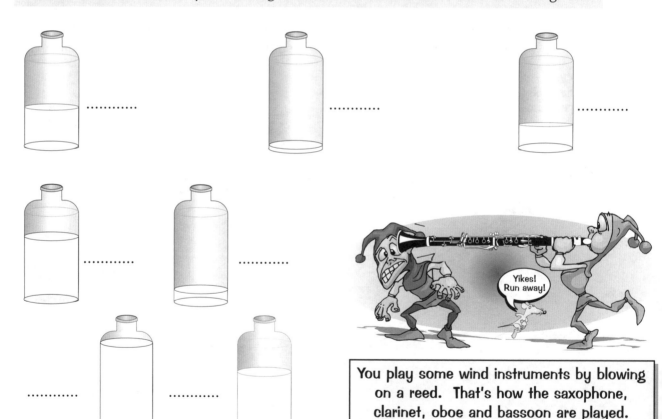

You play some wind instruments by blowing on a reed. That's how the saxophone, clarinet, oboe and bassoon are played.

Wind instruments — good vibrations...

You don't have to <u>just read</u> about stuff like this — why don't you <u>try</u> blowing across milk bottles with different amounts of water in. Then you'll see what I've been going on about all this time.

Why Bells Ring

Bells have two parts — the outside is either round or bell-shaped and is always made of metal. The other bit is either a tiny ball that rolls around inside, or a hammer that swings inside the bell.

Q1 Fill in the blanks to complete the paragraph about how bells ring.

When you shake a bell, the .... or .... inside knocks against the

outside. The noise is made by the .... bit on the outside which

.... when the hammer or ball hits it. The .... you shake the

bell, the more it vibrates and the .... it rings.

METAL	BALL		HAMMER
	LOUDER		
VIBRATES		HARDER	

Q2 The bigger the bell, the lower the sound it makes.
Circle the right words to complete the sentences.
I've done the first one for you.

A small bell will make a high / medium / low pitched sound.

A large bell will make a high / medium / low pitched sound.

A medium sized bell will make a high / medium / low pitched sound.

The smaller / larger a bell is, the higher the pitch when you ring it.

As Martin rang the bell, his feet disappeared.

Q3 For a) and b), number the bells in order of how high-pitched they are. Make the bell with the lowest pitch number one.

a)

b)

Hammers and balls — that rings a bell...

By now you might have figured out that for any instrument, the more of whatever's vibrating there is, the lower the pitch of the note. And the less there is, the higher. It's always true.

Revision Questions

Slapping, twanging, plucking, blowing and ringing — it's all about sound, how it's made and how it changes with <u>pitch</u> and <u>loudness</u>. When you've got all that sorted these questions should be simple.

Q1 If you bang a tuning fork against a solid object, does it make a ringing sound or a slapping sound?

....

Q2 What happens to the prongs of a tuning fork when it makes a sound?

....

Q3 What would happen if you banged a tuning fork against a solid object and then stuck it against a glass?

....

....

Q4 If the plumber whacks the short pipe Bernard can't hear it, but if he whacks the long pipe Bernard can hear it.

Bernard

Why can Bernard hear the long pipe being hit?

....

....

Q5 My alarm clock won't stop ringing. I want to wrap it up so I can't hear it. Put a tick next to each material below that would be good at muffling the sound.

☐ Newspaper   ☐ Tissue paper   ☐ Bubble wrap   ☐ A thick blanket

☐ 4 thick sleeping bags   ☐ Cling film   ☐ A thin sheet

Q6 Which of the things above would muffle the alarm best? ....

Q7 Finish off the sentence below by ⟨circling⟩ the right word from the brackets.

If you have two pieces of the same material the (THICKER / THINNER) one will muffle sound better.

Q8 ⟨Circle⟩ the right words from the brackets to make these sentences right.

Doing a 'fair test' means doing an experiment where you change only (ONE THING / TEN THINGS).

To test which material muffles sound best, you must only change the (MATERIAL / ALARM CLOCK).

1 page to go — no wonder I can't think of another joke...
DON'T PANIC. If you get stuck with any of these, look back through the book to help you — THEN PANIC.

Revision Questions

More lovely <u>questions</u> about sound with a great big bass guitar in the middle.

Q9 For each of these instruments, write 'high pitch' or 'low pitch' underneath its name.

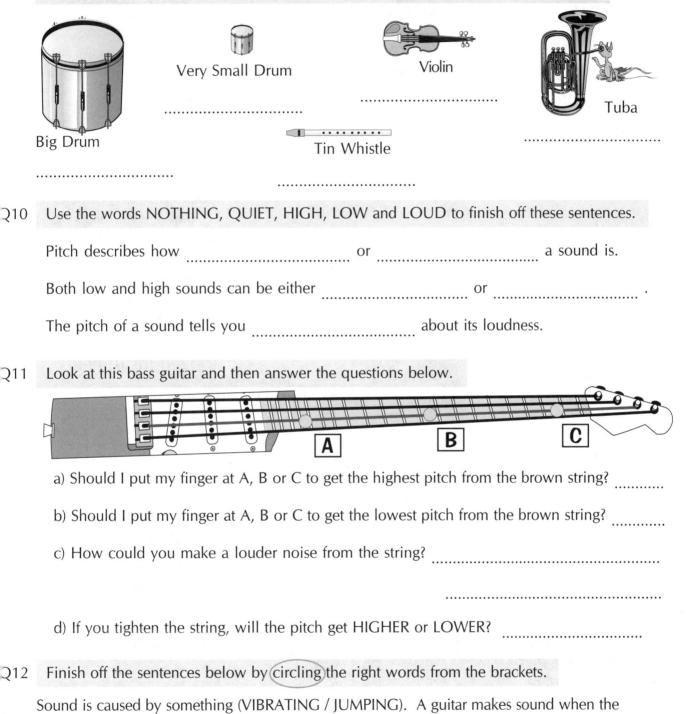

Very Small Drum

Violin

Tuba

Big Drum

Tin Whistle

....

....

....

....

Q10 Use the words NOTHING, QUIET, HIGH, LOW and LOUD to finish off these sentences.

Pitch describes how .... or .... a sound is.

Both low and high sounds can be either .... or ....

The pitch of a sound tells you .... about its loudness.

Q11 Look at this bass guitar and then answer the questions below.

A B C

a) Should I put my finger at A, B or C to get the highest pitch from the brown string? ....

b) Should I put my finger at A, B or C to get the lowest pitch from the brown string? ....

c) How could you make a louder noise from the string? ....

....

d) If you tighten the string, will the pitch get HIGHER or LOWER? ....

Q12 Finish off the sentences below by circling the right words from the brackets.

Sound is caused by something (VIBRATING / JUMPING). A guitar makes sound when the

plucked (TUNING PEGS / STRINGS) vibrate. When you beat a drum the (WORLD / SKIN) vibrates

to make the noise. In a wind instrument, it's the (AIR INSIDE / WATER INSIDE) that vibrates.

It's not over till the SAT lady sings...

It's the time when the drum beat slows and the instruments soften. All the questions are answered and the music of year five fades out... But what's that? — It's the pumping bass of year 6 science and it's coming this way...

Index